Born to

The Story of Rudolf Nureyev

Maureen Haselhurst

Contents

OXFORD
UNIVERSITY PRESS

UNIVERSITY PRESS

Great Clarendon Street, Oxford OX2 6DP

Oxford University Press is a department of the University of Oxford.
It furthers the University's objective of excellence in research, scholarship,
and education by publishing worldwide in

Oxford New York

Auckland Cape Town Dar es Salaam Hong Kong Karachi
Kuala Lumpur Madrid Melbourne Mexico City Nairobi
New Delhi Shanghai Taipei Toronto

With offices in

Argentina Austria Brazil Chile Czech Republic France Greece
Guatemala Hungary Italy Japan Poland Portugal Singapore
South Korea Switzerland Thailand Turkey Ukraine Vietnam
Oxford is a registered trade mark of Oxford University Press
in the UK and in certain other countries

British Library Cataloguing in Publication Data

Data available

ISBN: 978-0-19-919543-5

20 19 18 17 16 15 14

True Stories Pack 2 (one of each title) ISBN: 978-0-19-919545-9
True Stories Pack 2 Class Pack (six of each title) ISBN: 978-0-19-919544-2

Acknowledgements

The publisher would like to thank the following for permission
to reproduce photographs:

Milepost 92 1/2; Rex Features/Sipa: p 3; Rex Features/Ray Stevenson: p 30;
The Jim Henson Company: p 26.

Front cover background photo: Rex Features/SIPA
Inset photo: Corbis Sygma/Michael Childers
Back cover: Rex Features/Ray Stevenson

Illustrations are by Linda Clark
Maps are by Stefan Chabluk

Printed in China by Imago

Introduction

Rudolf Nureyev was a wonderful ballet dancer.

He grew up in Russia but he wanted to travel to other countries. He wanted the whole world to see him dance.

His name means "a beam of light" and his dazzling story is filled with adventure. This is how it happened …

Chapter 1

Born to Dance

In the bitter Russian winter of 1938 a baby was born on a train in a snowstorm.

Little Rudolf Nureyev came from a tribe of **Tartars**. They were **nomads** who wandered across Russia with their herds of fine horses.

They were proud people who fought fiercely and danced fiercely too!

The child born on the train would also grow to be hot-tempered and wander from place to place. He too would dance.

He would become one of the most brilliant ballet dancers that the world has known.

Rudolf was born on the Trans-Siberian train at Irkutsk.

Chapter 2

Music, Music, Music!

Rudolf was a year old when the **Second World War** began.

The family was **evacuated** to the drab Russian town of Ufa. Their home was a tiny flat on a cold, grey street.

This was an icy, dark and hungry world with only potatoes to eat.

Danger in this grim town wasn't only from war. After dark, wolves roamed the streets.

One night Rudolf's mother found herself in the middle of a snarling pack. Keeping a cool head, she struck a match and set fire to her shawl. The wolf pack fled!

However, it was in this unfriendly place that Rudolf discovered music. He would listen to it on their battered old radio and forget that he was cold and hungry.

He loved music – somehow it seemed to be part of him.

Chapter 3

Dance On!

Rudolf was small and frail and, because they were poor, he had to wear his sister's cast-offs. Because of this he was often bullied at school.

He threw tantrums and was only really happy in folk dance classes.

Soon he was doing concerts for wounded soldiers.

The moment that Rudolf saw his first ballet he knew that he was meant to dance. He was enchanted by the theatre and by the music. He loved the strong and yet delicate movements of the dancers.

He had heard of the famous ballet school in Leningrad. This was where he would go!

However, Rudolf's father thought that the ballet was no place for a boy. He beat the child every time he went to dancing class. Yet, nothing could stop Rudolf!

At 16, Rudolf joined the Ufa Ballet Company. He was rude and hot-tempered, but the other dancers and his teacher admired his amazing talent.

He danced with energy and power, but he was graceful and elegant too.

This boy was different!

Rudolf still dreamed of training at the Leningrad Ballet School.

At last he was given an **audition**. He arrived at the famous school with untidy hair and wearing his father's old army coat and boots. He looked totally out of place – until he danced. Rudolf was accepted into the school!

Chapter 4

The Rebel

In Leningrad Rudolf broke all the strict ballet school rules. At night he would sneak out of the **dormitory** and go to see the famous Kirov Ballet.

Now he dreamed another dream. He would join the Kirov and travel.

For three years he practised without rest until every step was perfect.

Rudolf was never going to be allowed to travel abroad unless he obeyed the rules. Only well-behaved dancers were trusted to leave the country.

However, he was chosen to dance in Moscow. He performed brilliantly and the audience went wild. A new ballet star was on the rise!

At last Rudolf's light was beginning to shine.

Rudolf's dream came true. He joined the Kirov Ballet Company and thrilled his audiences.

Still there were strict rules to keep. The dancers were not allowed to speak to foreigners and were told to spy on one another. Rudolf knew all about **spies** – his father had been one!

So, Rudolf did the opposite. He learned English and spoke to every foreigner he met.

At last, at the age of 23, he was allowed to go on tour to Paris and London.

However, Russia was a powerful country that didn't trust other countries. So the Secret Police sent their spies to follow Rudolf – they knew all about the rebel. He would be watched!

Chapter 5

Dangerous Behaviour

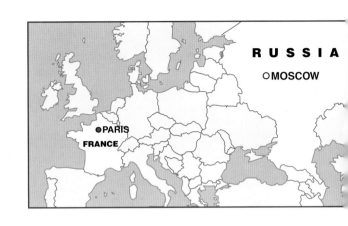

Paris went wild for Rudolf and Rudolf went wild in Paris! The audiences were dazzled by his dancing.

He loved being a star. He bought trendy clothes and ate in expensive restaurants with French and English friends.

However, the Russian spies were watching his every move.

Back in Moscow, the Secret Police were told of Rudolf's behaviour. The Kirov Ballet Company was told to send him home.

However, Rudolf was the Kirov's star. As long as he was dancing on stage, the theatre was packed. If Rudolf went then so would the fans.

The instruction was ignored!

The Secret Police again demanded that he be returned. Again they were ignored.

The third message arrived with two **burly** Russian spies. Rudolf was to be stopped at the airport in Paris before he could fly to London. He was to be taken back to Russia, by force if necessary.

Chapter 6

A Dance to Freedom

The Kirov ballet dancers were boarding the plane for London when the spies appeared. They informed Rudolf that he was needed in Moscow to dance.

Rudolf was horrified. He knew it was a lie. He knew it meant prison! Even worse, he'd never be allowed to dance again. He would rather die!

From across the airport building someone called his name. There, among a group of his fans, was Clara Saint, one of the friends he'd made in Paris.

Pulling away from the two spies, he went over to her and quickly whispered what was going on. Clara knew exactly what to do.

Upstairs was the office of the French Airport Police. They were astonished when Clara dashed in, shouting that Rudolf Nureyev was about to be dragged back to Russia!

The policemen then made the decision that would change the world of dance forever. They would help!

Rudolf was trapped between the Russian spies when Clara coolly walked up to him.

Pretending to be his girlfriend, she kissed him and whispered the plan. Rudolf understood.

Without warning, he broke away from the Russians and ran towards the Airport Police office. He fled through the back door and into freedom!

Chapter 7

Rudi Mania!

Paris was no longer safe for Rudolf. He was afraid of being kidnapped. So he joined the Royal Ballet Company in London.

Here he danced with the famous **ballerina** Margot Fonteyn. They were the most perfect dancing partners. Wherever they danced the audience went wild.

Rudolf danced all over the world, mixing with royalty, presidents and film stars. Ballet was cool – it was part of the "**Swinging Sixties**".

Rudolf loved the fame and the fans who adored him. In his trendy clothes, he was a ballet pop star. Rudi Mania was everywhere.

Rudolf was as famous as Miss Piggy and Kermit the Frog!

Yet Rudolf never felt safe for spies still followed him. He was very nearly caught on board an aeroplane. Luckily Rudolf spotted the spies before they spotted him. He slipped into a toilet and hid there for the rest of the flight!

Chapter 8

The Final Years

Now Rudolf was hugely wealthy and loved buying beautiful things. He owned splendid houses with fabulous furniture.

Yet, wherever he went he took what he called his "doggy bag". Inside were his dance shoes, his tights, his stage make-up and a toy train. These were the only things that he really needed.

He travelled without rest, dancing all over the world for his adoring fans.

But Rudolf was ill. He began to dance badly. Sometimes he had to stop and sit down. Audiences would boo and demand their money back.

Yet his pride was still there. He wouldn't and couldn't stop dancing!

Rudolf takes a bow after another great performance.

In 1993, the beam of light went out.

Rudolf Nureyev was dead. He left a large fortune. More importantly, ordinary people all over the world now loved the ballet.

Perhaps his beam of light had not gone out after all.

Glossary

audition   a test to see if someone is good enough to perform on the stage

ballerina   a female ballet dancer

burly   big and strong

dormitory   a bedroom with many beds

evacuate   to move someone away from danger

nomads   people who move from place to place in search of food for their animals

rebel   someone who takes no notice of rules

Second World War   the time between 1939 and 1945 when most of the world was at war

spies   people who secretly watch other people

"Swinging Sixties"   the 1960s when there were exciting changes in ideas, clothes and music

Tartars   a wandering tribe who lived in the middle of Asia

Index

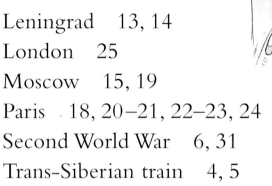